W9-BXU-873

Never Talk to Strangers

A Book About Personal Safety

By Irma Joyce
Illustrated by George Buckett

A GOLDEN BOOK • NEW YORK
Western Publishing Company, Inc., Racine, Wisconsin 53404

If you are hanging from a trapeze
And up sneaks a camel with bony knees,
Remember this rule, if you please—
    Never talk to strangers.

If you are shopping in a store
And a spotted leopard leaps through the door,
Don't ask him what he's shopping for.
　　Never talk to strangers.

If the doorbell rings and standing there
Is a grouchy, grumbling grizzly bear,
Don't open the door; Mom won't care.
Never talk to strangers.

If you are in the park for a walk
And out of a cloud parachutes a hawk,
Unless you know his name, don't talk.
Never talk to strangers.

If you are waiting for a bus
And behind you stands a rhinoceros,

Though he may shove and make a fuss,
Never talk to strangers.

If you are out for a mountain climb
And a coyote asks if you know the time,
Let him wait for a clock to chime.
    Never talk to strangers.

If you're mailing a letter to Aunt Lucille
And you see a car with a whale at the wheel,
Stay away from him and his automobile.
Never talk to strangers.

If you are riding your bike at noon
And you see a bee with a bass bassoon,

Don't stop to ask the name of his tune.
Never talk to strangers.

If you are swimming in a pool
And a crocodile begins to drool,
Paddle away and repeat this rule—
Never talk to strangers.

But...if your father introduces you
To a roly-poly kangaroo,
Say politely, "How do you do?"
   That's not talking to strangers,
   Because your family knows her.

If your teacher says she'd like you to meet
A lilac llama who's very sweet,

Invite her over and serve a treat.
That's not talking to strangers,
Because your teacher knows her.

If a pal of yours you've always known
Brings around a prancing roan,
Welcome him in a friendly tone.

That's not talking to strangers,
Because your pal knows him.

If while eating toast and honey,
You look around and see a bunny,

That means it's spring...and if it's sunny,
Look outside, but don't yell, "Hey,"
Just enjoy the pretty day.

Do you know why you've never heard
This jolly giraffe say a single word?
It's because she learned from a little bird—
Never talk to strangers!